Scott Joplin

(1868–1917)

RAGTIMES

for piano • für Klavier • pour piano

Könemann Music Budapest

K 140

The Easy Winners

Not fast

A Breeze From Alabama

The Sycamore

The Cascades

Maple Leaf Rag

Tempo di marcia

Palm Leaf Rag

Play a little slow

Something Doing

Swipesy

CAKE WALK

Reflection Rag

Slow march tempo

38

Peacherine Rag

The Ragtime Dance

Not too fast

Notice: To get the desired effect of "Stop Time", the pianist will please stamp the heel of one foot heavily upon the floor at the word "Stamp". Do not raise the toe from the floor while stamping.

Stamp Stamp Stamp Stamp Stamp Stamp Stamp Stamp

Stamp Stamp Stamp Stamp Stamp Stamp Stamp Stamp

Stamp Stamp Stamp Stamp Stamp Stamp Stamp Stamp

Stamp Stamp Stamp Stamp Stamp Stamp Stamp Stamp

Stamp Stamp Stamp Stamp Stamp Stamp Stamp Stamp

Lily Queen

Heliotrope Bouquet

Slow march tempo

Leola

Slow march tempo

Elite Syncopations

The Entertainer

The Strenuous Life

Not fast

Sunflower Slow Drag

The Chrysanthemum

Slow march tempo

78

Original Rags

84

Eugenia

Slow march tempo ♩=72

The Favorite

Slow march tempo

The Nonpareil

Sensation

Weeping Willow

Not fast

The Augustan Club Waltzes

Binks' Waltz

Bethena

Pleasant Moments

Slow waltz time

Harmony Club Waltz

Introduction
Andante

dal segno % al Fine

Combination March

Antoinette

Tempo di marcia

Cleopha

The Rosebud March

146

The Crush Collision March

The noise of trains while running at the rate of sixty miles per hour,   Whistling for the crossing,

Noise of the trains   Whistle before the collision   The collision

March Majestic

Tempo di marcia

INDEX

© 1994 for this edition by Könemann Music Budapest Kft.
H–1093 Budapest, Közraktár utca 10.

K 140/5

Distributed worldwide by
Könemann Verlagsgesellschaft mbH, Bonner Str. 126.
D–50968 Köln

Responsible co-editor: István Máriássy
Production: Detlev Schaper
Cover design: Peter Feierabend
Technical editor: Dezső Varga

Printed by Kossuth Printing House Co., Budapest
Printed in Hungary

ISBN 963 8303 53 0

URTEXT

Carl Philipp Emanuel Bach:

Sämtliche Klavierwerke in 14 Bänden
Complete Piano Works in 14 volumes
(Leinenband in 3 Schuber – *cloth-bound in 3 slipcase*)

I 1. Die 6 Preussischen Sonaten,
 Die 6 Württembergischen Sonaten
 2. 6 Sonatinen, 6 Sonaten mit veränderten Reprisen
 3. 6 Sonaten (Erste Fortsetzung),
 6 Sonaten (Zweite Fortsetzung)
 4. 18 Probestücke in 6 Sonaten, 6 Sonatine nuove,
 6 leichte Sonaten, 6 Sonaten (Damensonaten)

Johann Sebastian Bach:

Sämtliche Klavierwerke in 13 Bänden
Complete Piano Works in 13 volumes

Das wohltemperierte Klavier I–II
Englische Suiten
Fantasien
Französische Suiten
Inventionen, Kleine Präludien und Fughetten
Klavierübung I (6 Partiten)
Klavierübung II–IV (Italienisches Konzert, Französische
 Ouverture, 4 Duette, Goldberg-Variationen)
Konzertbearbeitungen
Toccaten

IN VORBEREITUNG – *IN PREPARATION*
Einzelstücke II

Mily Balakirev:

Sämtliche Klavierwerke in 5 Bänden
Complete Piano Works in 5 volumes

Ludwig van Beethoven:

Sämtliche Klavierwerke in 9 Bänden
Complete Piano Works in 9 volumes

Klavierstücke und Bagatelle
Rondi, Kleine Sonaten, Sonatinen
Sonaten I–II–III
Tänze
Variationen I–II–III
Sonaten (1. Leinenband, 2. Pappband im Schuber)
 Sonatas (1. Cloth-bound, 2. Soft-cover, slipcase)
Piano Complete (1. Leinenband, 2. Pappband im Schuber;
 1. Cloth-bound, 2. Soft-cover, slipcase)

Johannes Brahms:

Sämtliche Klavierwerke in 5 Bänden
Complete Piano Works in 5 volumes

Fantasien, Intermezzi und Klavierstücke
Scherzo, Balladen, Rhapsodien und Tänze
Sonaten
Variationen
5 Studien, 51 Übungen
Piano Complete (1. Leinenband, 2. Pappband im Schuber;
 1. Cloth-bound, 2. Soft-cover, slipcase)

Frédéric Chopin:

Sämtliche Klavierwerke in 11 Bänden
Complete Piano Works in 11 volumes

Ballades
Etudes
Mazurkas
Nocturnes
Polonaises
Scherzos
Sonates
Valses
24 Préludes, Impromptus
IN VORBEREITUNG – *IN PREPARATION*
Individual Pieces

Claude Debussy:

Sämtliche Klavierwerke in 5 Bänden
Complete Piano Works in 5 volumes

Children's Corner and Individual Pieces
Suite Bergamasque, Pour le piano, Estampes
12 Etudes
24 Préludes
IN VORBEREITUNG – *IN PREPARATION*
Images

Antonín Dvořák:

Sämtliche Klavierwerke I–II
Complete Piano Works I–II

Mikhail Glinka:

Sämtliche Klavierwerke in 2 Bänden
Complete Piano Works in 2 volumes

Edvard Grieg:

Sämtliche Klavierwerke in 5 Bänden
Complete Piano Works in 5 volumes

Holberg-Suite und Liedbearbeitungen
 ~ and Song Arrangements
Lyrische Stücke – *Lyrical Pieces*
Norwegische Volksweisen und Tänze –
 Norwegian Folksongs and Dances
Peer Gynt und andere Bearbeitungen eigener Werke
 ~ and other arrangements of own works
Sonate und Klavierstücke – *Sonata and Piano Pieces*
Piano Complete (1. Leinenband, 2. Pappband im Schuber;
 1. Cloth-bound, 2. Soft-cover, slipcase)

Joseph Haydn:

Sämtliche Klavierwerke in 5 Bänden
Complete Piano Works in 5 volumes

Klavierstücke I
Klavierstücke II (Arrangements)
Sonaten I–II–III
Piano Complete (1. Leinenband, 2. Pappband im Schuber;
 1. Cloth-bound, 2. Soft-cover, slipcase)

Franz Liszt:

Ausgewählte Klavierwerke I–II
Selected Piano Pieces I–II

Anatoly Lyadov:

Sämtliche Klavierwerke in 4 Bänden
Complete Piano Works in 4 volumes

Felix Mendelssohn-Bartholdy:

Sämtliche Klavierwerke in 9 Bänden
Complete Piano Works in 9 volumes

Lieder ohne Worte I–III
IN VORBEREITUNG – *IN PREPARATION*
Etüden und Variationen

Wolfgang Amadeus Mozart:

Sämtliche Klavierwerke in 4 Bänden
Complete Piano Works in 4 volumes

Klavierstücke
Sonaten, Fantasien und Rondi I–II
Variationen
Piano Complete (1. Leinenband, 2. Pappband im Schuber;
 1. Cloth-bound, 2. Soft-cover, slipcase)

Modest Musorgsky:

Sämtliche Klavierwerke
Complete Piano Works

Henry Purcell:

Sämtliche Klavierwerke in 2 Bänden
Complete Piano Works in 2 volumes

Individual Pieces
Suites
Piano Complete

Franz Schubert:

Klavierstücke I (Fantasien, Variationen und
 Klavierstücke)
Klavierstücke II (Ungarische Melodie, Impromptus,
 Moments Musicaux, 3 Klavierstücke)
Tänze I–II

Robert Schumann:

Album für die Jugend, Kinderszenen –
 Album for the Young, Scenes from Childhood

Alexander Skryabin:

Sämtliche Klavierwerke in 8 Bänden
Complete Piano Works in 8 volumes
Etudes
Individual Piano Pieces
Mazurkas & Valses
Poèmes & Impromptus
Préludes I–II
Sonatas I–II

Pyotr Tchaikovsky:

Sämtliche Klavierwerke in 7 Bänden
Complete Piano Works in 7 volumes
Klavierstücke – *Piano Pieces* I–II–III
Sonatas
The Seasons and Children's Album
18 Klavierstücke – *18 Piano Pieces,* Op. 72
IN VORBEREITUNG – *IN PREPARATION*
Individual Pieces

19th Century Russian Composers I

(Borodin, Cui, Rimsky-Korsakov)

20th Century Russian Composers

TASCHENPARTITUREN (Leinenband)
STUDY SCORE EDITIONS (cloth-bound)

Johann Sebastian Bach:
Das wohltemperierte Klavier I–II
Französische und Englische Suiten
Inventionen, Sinfonien, Kleine Präludien und
Fughetten
Klavierübung I–IV
Toccaten, Fantasien

Ludwig van Beethoven:
Piano Solo, Complete Edition (im Schuber – *slipcase*)
32 Klaviersonaten (im Schuber – *slipcase*)
Kleinere Klavierwerke
Variationen

Johannes Brahms:
Piano Solo, Complete Edition (im Schuber – *slipcase*)
Klavierstücke
Sonaten, Variationen, 51 Übungen

Edvard Grieg:
Piano Solo, Complete Edition (im Schuber – *slipcase*)

Joseph Haydn:
Piano Solo, Complete Edition (im Schuber – *slipcase*)

Wolfgang Amadeus Mozart:
Piano Solo, Complete Edition (im Schuber – *slipcase*)

Modest Musorgsky:
Piano Solo, Complete Edition

Henry Purcell:
Piano Solo, Complete Edition

LIEDER – *SONGS*

Franz Schubert:

Die schöne Müllerin
Winterreise